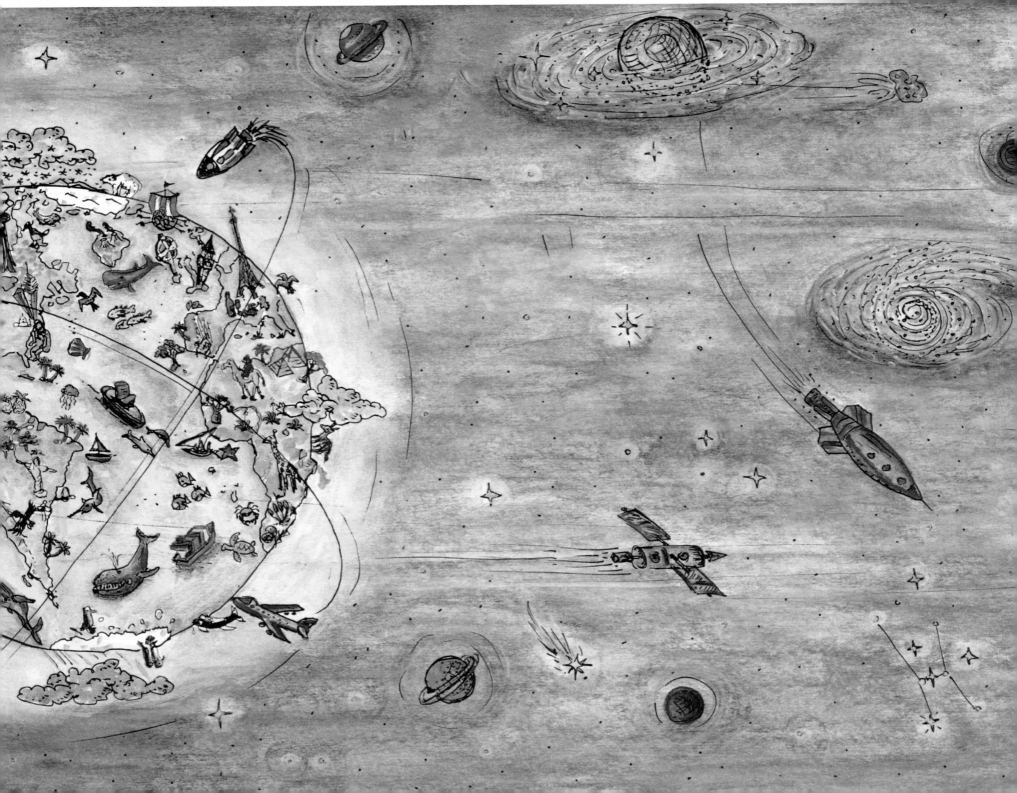

Dedicated to those who move, those who care and those left behind

Special thank you to Guillaume, David and Paul for their patient support.

To the Moon
A story of change and transition

written by Anders Granberg   illustrated by Lukas Angst

Today is different, I can just feel it in the air. Today everyone is busy with something to do. What is happening and why am I feeling so confused?

My parents have some big news. I wait and wait, as patiently as I can. I think it lasted three seconds though how can I tell? Waiting is boring and I want to know now. I feel like I am on my tippy-toes with energy and need.

We are going to move! It is a new adventure and they are excited and say; "it will be great!". But inside I feel all tangled and jumbled, sad and excited and my tummy has started to hurt. Why am I worried when everyone is smiling and rushing? I have so many questions and very few answers.

"The moon!" they exclaim, "we are moving to the moon!" How can we live there when it is so far away? How will we get there and how will I know what to do? Is there a school? Will there be friends or will I be alone? I miss feeling safe and it feels like butterflies are taking over my stomach.

I screamed at my puppy today, it is all his fault! Why do we have to go? I feel so comfortable here. I know where everything is, from the tallest tree to climb to the most clever hiding places for hide-and-seek. Will I ever find that again?

The puppy is not really at fault and he listens so well. My brain is all foggy, so he keeps my stories and ideas for now. He remembers the time when we explored the abandoned house and when I flew my kite with friends on a windy, stormy day. I am glad I have my puppy when the world is going crazy!

I have to say my goodbyes to everyone I know and even those who I do not. I will miss them lots and I want to keep in touch. How does one cross empty space to connect with people? All this means that I feel so small. What can I create to keep my memories together?

My friends were the hardest goodbyes; they broke down in large tears. How can we lose each other? I will really miss them and find it hard to let go. I carry them with me; Alexandra and Thomas, and Ahmed and Caofai too. Even snotty-nosed Dennis is important to me. They all have a space in my heart when I think of my move.

Talking calms the butterflies and maybe even a drawing or two. My parents are helpful and answer my questions. Throughout it all, my puppy is there. He helps me to think and take a few deep breaths. I find love and security in the moment, to keep going when everything feels upside-down.

Then it is time to pack and get ready for the big move. What will I need and how can I get ready? It is so far across the sky. Will I be able to pack my toys and take my puppy? How will we send things? What about all the stuff I need?

I search for clues about the moon to help on my journey. So many new adventures, I want to research some more. The moon has so many holes and no gravity too. What will the new place look like and how can I prepare? How do I say hello and thank you in moon language to connect and do more?

There will be a new school with new children for sure! Children I can play with and new things to explore. What will I say to connect and make friends? What can I play and what are my favourite games? How did I meet my old friends? I am sure I will connect to others, both similar and new.

I imagine my future, living on the moon. It will be different and even the food will not be the same. I hope they have less broccoli and beans, but I am not sure. I will find things I like and some I do not. Each new change will be a challenge. I know or at least I am ready to try.

Today is still different and I
am still finding out more. I feel
prepared and scared, excited
and worried, still on my tippy-
toes, but ready to go. The moon knows I am
coming and I will be there, with my bag full of
memories, my family and my puppy. Together
and ready, for the new adventure ahead.

For parents

Moving with children is challenging. We wanted to offer this book as a tool to support families to prepare for transitions and changes. We hope it can support moments of fun and hilarity whilst delving into potential fears and sadness. We have left space on pages for notes and memories as well as some mediation drawings for children to colour in.

Here are some ideas for supporting a healthy transition amidst busy moves:

In preparation:

- Start talking about the transition in advance. Younger children may only need a few weeks notice whilst older children may need a few months to encourage time for discussion and reflection.
- Give children the opportunity to say their goodbyes and help children to think about people, places and objects that have meant something in their current location. Often creating a keepsake, a photo album or do something else creative to help the child feel connected and this can be helpful to tangibly remember your current home.
- Find age-appropriate ways to involve children in the moving process. For example, ask the children to choose a few comforting items to keep and pack into their own bag, luggage or suitcases.
- Highlight the benefits your new location has to offer and research your destination. The phrase "new home" might help to distinguish from your leaving place or old home.

After moving:

- Enjoy quiet weekends with family time as often children need additional attention after a move. Expect mood swings as at the moment so much is out of the child's control. After a move they may become clingy and fearful and act younger again.
- Continue to communicate with those that have been left behind and use the memory keepsake to connect with feelings and people.
- If your child is going to be attending a new daycare or school, go and visit before the first day. Take your child to visit a new school at least once before their first day. Meet their teacher and let them see the classroom.
- Stick to familiar routines wherever you are and maintain a sense of normalcy. Simple daily rituals like sitting together at mealtimes, reading stories before bed, and playing familiar games, give security and help to process change.
- Keep talking with your children and be honest about your own feelings. Slow down as children will take their cues for feelings from parents and role-model a reflective change

We wish you all the best with your new family adventure.

Talking about moving can be difficult and we wanted to offer an opportunity to do some calming colouring in during the discussion. This can be helpful for opening up a deeper discussion about feelings and emotions.